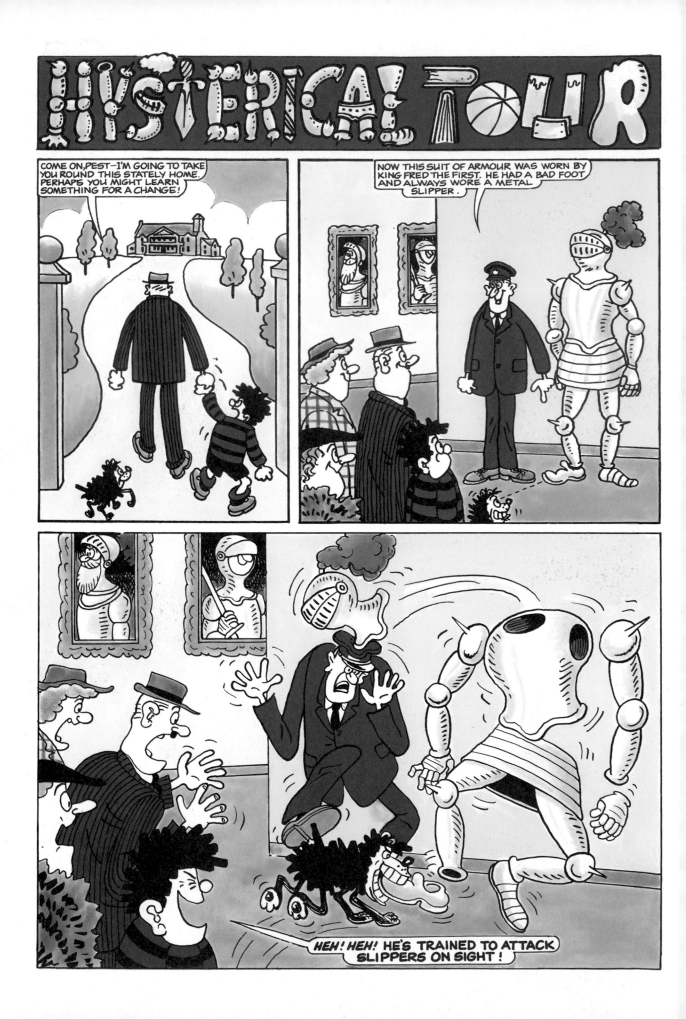

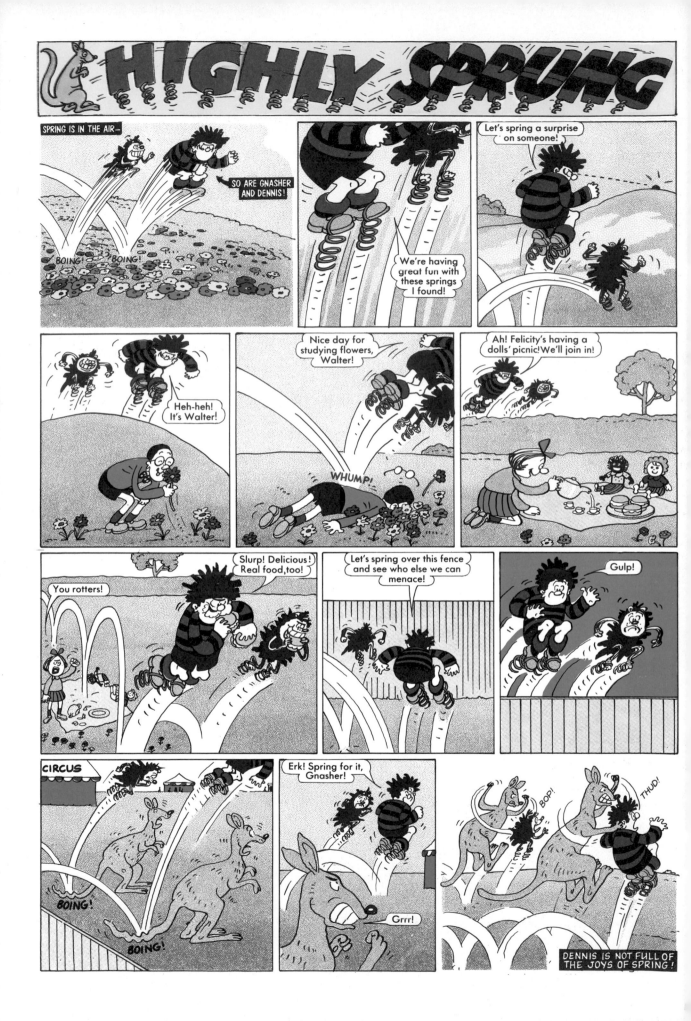

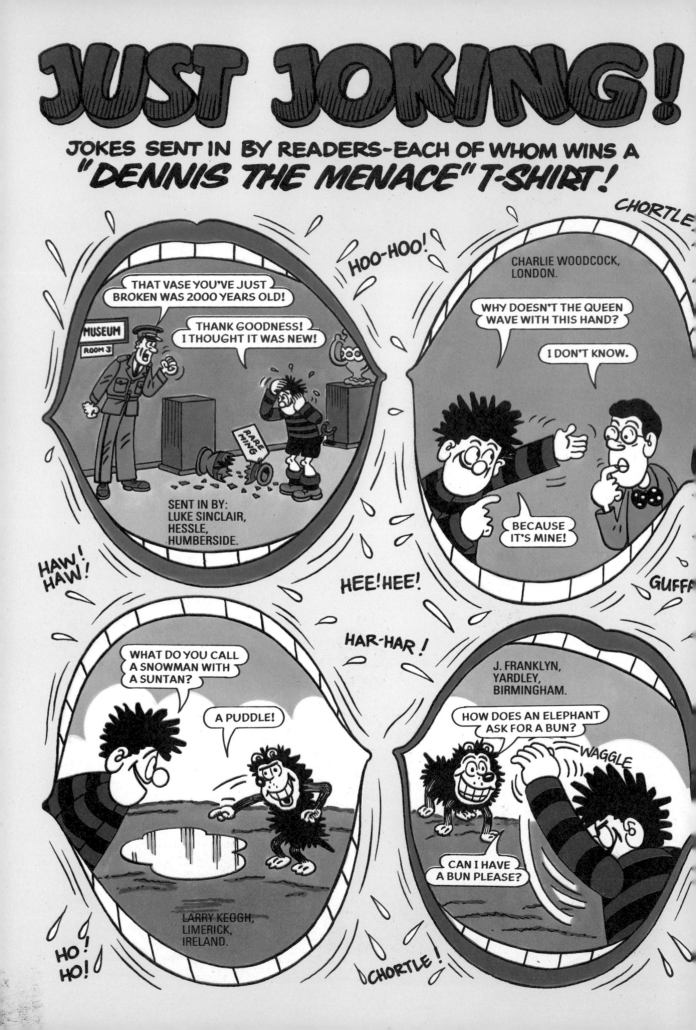

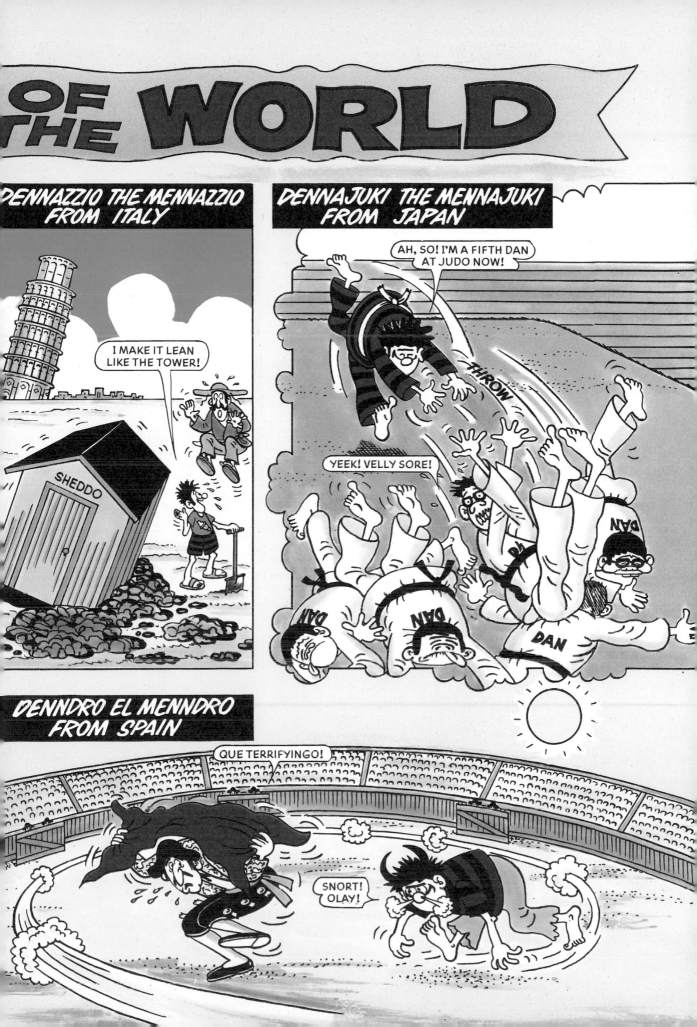

LOUT of AFRICA

"**G**ROAN! Wish I didn't have my geography exam coming up!" said Dennis testily as he left the house. "I don't know a thing about Darkest Africa."

"But I do!" a voice said darkly. Suddenly a khaki clad figure popped up above the six foot high fence Dennis was passing.

"It's Stanley Livingstone, my explorer neighbour. My, how you've grown!" gasped a highly surprised Dennis.

"Actually, I got a bit of help from my loyal crocodile, Carruthers. He's better than a stepladder," said Stanley loftily.

"I'm off exploring Africa after breakfast. Would you and Gnasher like to come along as my assistants?"

"We'll start right away by assisting you with your breakfast," volunteered Dennis helpfully, and soon they were all tucking into elephantburger sandwiches.

"I suppose we'd better be off then," said Stanley crustily as he finished the last of his sandwich. "We're going in search of the Lost Tribe of the Lost River of the Lost Valley of Umwongo. I did have a map of the area once . . . "

"Where is it now?" questioned Dennis.

"Er — I LOST it!" admitted Stanley, his face dropping. He picked it up again and packed it with the rest of his equipment in his tri-plane — so called because you had to "tri" very hard to get it airborne.

A fast dash down Stanley's garden and they were up in the wide blue yonder — actually a pair of Dennis's Mum's wide blue curtains which they became entangled with as they took off. They quickly cut themselves free using the latest invention to replace solar power, MOLAR power, provided by Gnasher and Carruthers.

"Africa here we come!" yelled Dennis to Mum as they took off again. "I might be a bit late home for tea!"

After several hairy moments (due to the fact that Gnasher was moulting), they spotted Africa far below them . . . then not so far below them . . . then very very near them. "We're run out of fuel!" shrieked Stanley, his voice falling along with the rest of him. Fortunately the plane came down on a basking water buffalo, then a basking elephant, then a basking rhino as it trampolined to a halt in a water-hole in the middle of dense jungle (it must be said the occupants of the plane weren't too bright either).

DONK!

BONK!

BOOMF!

"W-we're trapped! T-trapped, I t-tell you! There's no way through the j-jungle!" stammered St-St-St-Stanley.

"Fear not, Stan old man. Gnasher has recently started eating vegetarian food," said Dennis calmly as the waves from the splash-down subsided.

With that Gnasher started clearing the undergrowth with his razor sharp fangs faster than Carl Lewis with his shorts on fire.

Eventually they came to a river where a native was just completing a dug-out canoe with a spade.

"Can you direct me to the Lost Tribe of the Lost River of the Lost Valley of Umwongo?" quizzed Stanley.

"I'm at a loss to do so, but climb aboard my boat and I'll take you to someone who might be able to help," replied the native.

At that moment Carruthers the crocodile was feeling peckish.

"I'm starving!" he thought with a hollow laugh, and with that he took a large bite out of the boat.

"You've eaten the back of the boat!" said Dennis sternly. "You'll have to carry us down the river on your back now."

Off they sailed with a good head of steam (Dennis had given Carruthers a few extra-strong peppermints for the journey).

STRONG MINTS

D

At length they came upon a large building on the banks of the river. Dennis read the notice outside — LOST PROPERTY OFFICE.

"This is your stop!" said the native, lashing Carruthers' tail to a jetty. Inside the building a small man stood behind a hippopotamus, as desks weren't available in this part of the jungle.

"We're looking for the Lost Tribe of the Lost River of the Lost Valley of the Umwongo."

"Here we are, sir!" said the small man pointing to a cobweb covered group on a high shelf. "Rather careless of you to lose them, if I may say so!"

One long journey later Dennis arrived back home — just in time for his geography exam. What bad timing!

"Where are the Umwongo tribe found?" asked Teacher, reading from his exam questions.

And believe it or not, Dennis was the only pupil in the class to get the answer right.

EXAM ANSWERS
THE UMWONGO
TRIBE CAN BE
FOUND AT MY
HOUSE — THEY'VE
COME OVER FOR
A HOLIDAY.

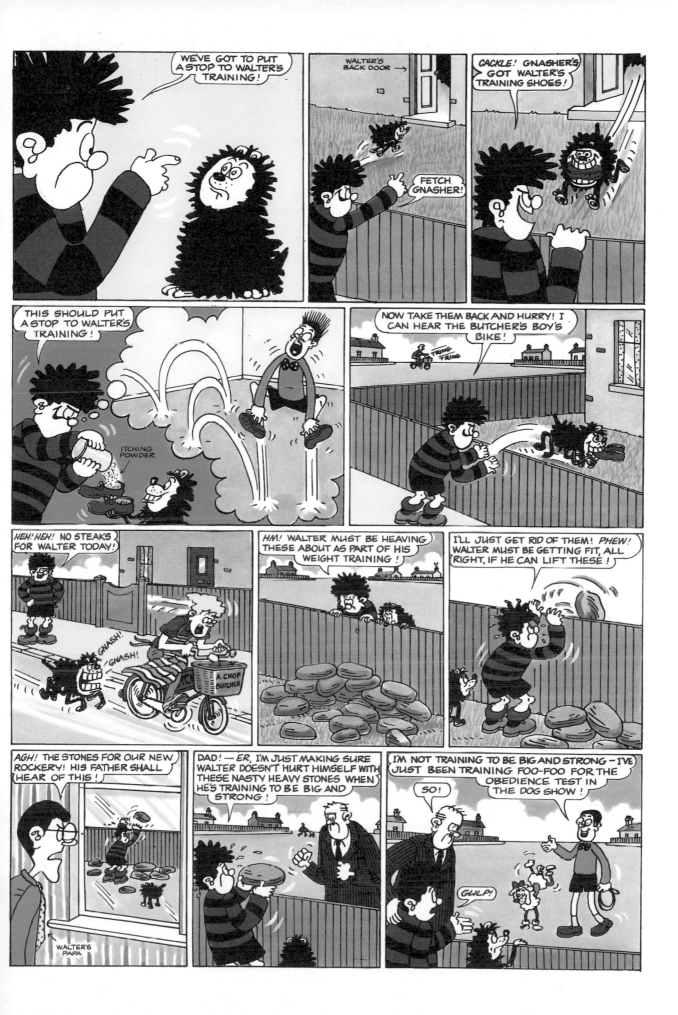